Kindergarten
Learning About God

by Cherie Noel

PositiveAction
BIBLE CURRICULUM

Kindergarten: Learning About God

Written by Cherie Noel

Copyright © 1990, 2004, 2010 by Positive Action for Christ , Inc., P.O. Box 700, 502 W. Pippen, Whitakers, NC 27891. All rights reserved. No part may be reproduced in any manner without permission in writing from the publisher.

www.positiveaction.org

Third Edition, 2010
Third Printing, 2014

Printed in the United States of America

ISBN: 978-1-59557-061-1

Curriculum Consultant: Helen Boen
Editor: CJ Harris
Layout and Design: Shannon Brown
Artwork: Julie Speer

Published by

PositiveAction
BIBLE CURRICULUM

conTenTS

Trace the broken lines to complete the wings of the butterfly.
Color both wings alike.

Complete the numbers to show the correct order.

We work.

We play.

We rest.

God Cares For His Creation

ALL Things were made by God (John 1:3).

Cut out the pictures of the things God created and paste them in the correct boxes.

Day 1	Day 2
Day 3	Day 4
Day 5	Day 6

God gives us all things to enjoy (1 Timothy 6:17).

Draw birds, fish, flowers, and a tree to complete the picture.

Draw 3   Draw 2   Draw 4   Draw 1

Lesson 2 Cutouts

Lesson Three
Adam And Eve

Cross out the pictures showing wrong actions.
Color the pictures showing children obeying God's Word.

Obey God Always.

Complete the outline of the tree. Draw and color more fruit on the tree.
Each time you draw some fruit, let it remind you to obey always.
Trace the broken lines to complete the sentence.

Obey God.

Cain And Abel

God made families.

MOTHER **CHILDREN** **FATHER**

Cut out the picture of the fruit and paste it in Cain's arms.
Paste the picture of the lamb in Abel's arms.

AbeL **Cain**

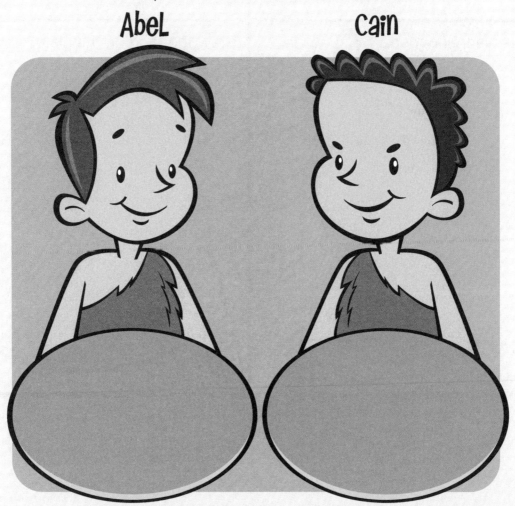

God gives us food.

Color these pictures.

Draw the seeds.

Draw the water and small plants.

Draw the plant and food.

Draw the food on the plate.

The Story Of Noah

These two animals are slow. Help them find a shortcut to the ark.

Noah obeys God.

Draw a line from each picture to the correct number to show the order in which these events occurred.

1

2

3

4

Lesson Six
The Tower Of BabeL

Connect the dots to complete the Tower of Babel, then color the tower.

Do you remember?

Color the pictures.

Lesson Seven
Abraham And Isaac

Draw a line from each picture to the correct number to show the order in which these events occurred.

1

2

3

4

God made me special.

Draw a picture of yourself.

Draw your favorite food.

Draw your favorite activity.

Jacob And Esau

Cut out and paste pictures of Jacob and Esau below.

Jacob

Esau

Color these pictures.

Circle the cookies you will give to your friend.

Share what you have.

Take Turns.

Lesson 8 cutouts

Joseph And His New Coat

Color the picture.

How many brothers did Joseph have?_____

Draw lines to match the pictures that belong together.

Lesson Ten
Joseph In Egypt

God had a plan for Joseph.

Draw lines to match the pictures with the numbers to show the order in which these events happened.

1

2

3

4

Be kind.

Cross out the picture that does not show kindness. Color the other pictures.

A New Girl In Class

Watching My Baby Sister

Helping My Mom

Lesson Eleven
Moses And The Princess

Color the basket brown. Color the blanket purple.
Color the water blue. Color baby Moses.

God is always with us.

In the blank space, draw a picture of another place where God will be with you.
Color the pictures.

God Speaks To Moses

Draw the flames on the bush and color them red and yellow.
Then color the rest of the bush.

God's Word is True.

Connect the dots to draw a picture of the Bible.
Then complete the words on the Bible.

Israel In The Desert

Color the picture with the cloud. Make it daytime.
Color the picture with the fire. Make it nighttime.

Color the things that remind you of Moses.
Of whom do the other things remind you?

Joshua And Jericho

Trace the broken lines to show where the Israelites marched each day.

Each day for six days the people walked around the city one time.

WhaT happened To The ciTy of Jericho?

Connect the dots to complete the picture.

On the seventh day the people walked around the city seven times.
Then they shouted and blew trumpets.

Lesson Fifteen
Sampson—God's Strong Man

Color the picture by number.

| 1–Blue | 2–Red | 3–Gray | 4–Flesh | 5–Brown | 6–Purple | 7–Yellow |

Draw lines to match the beginning of the story on
the left with the end of the story on the right.

King Solomon

Trace the broken lines to complete the other side of the great temple Solomon built.
Then color the temple.

God wants us to have godly character in our lives.

Cut out the pictures of fruit and paste them in the cornucopia. Each fruit represents a godly character trait. Then draw a line from the character trait to the fruit listed with each trait.

Pineapple (Goodness)	Pear (Faith)	Orange (Love)	Apple (Joy)	Pumpkin (Kindness)	Grapes (Peace)

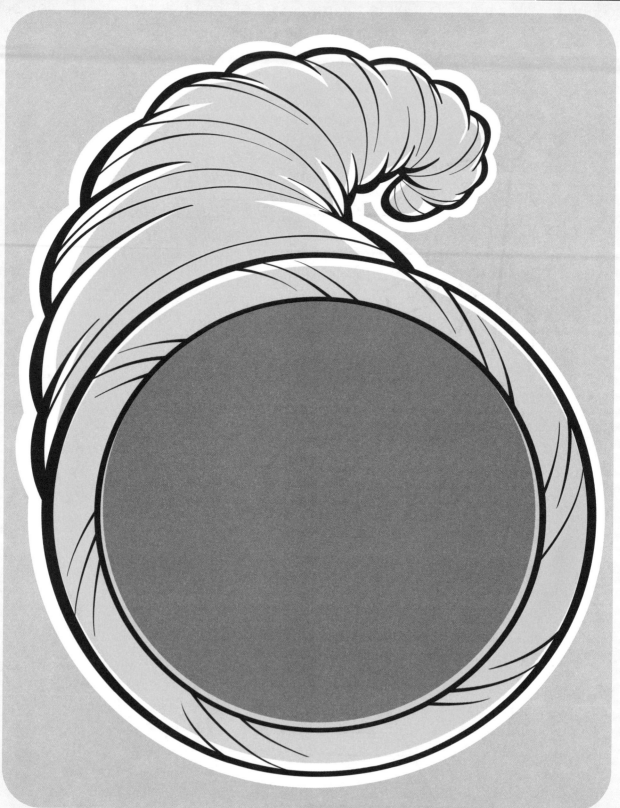

42

Lesson 16 cutouts

Lesson Seventeen
Elisha The Prophet

Help Naaman find Elisha's house. Then help him find the river.

LiTTLe children can serve God.

Cut out the pictures and paste them in the correct order to tell the story.

Daniel And His Friends

Connect the dots to complete the picture of Nebuchadnezzar's golden image.

Do not be afraid (Deuteronomy 31:6).

Color the picture of the fourth person in the fiery furnace with Daniel's three friends. Color the flames **red** and **yellow**. Then color the smoke **dark gray**.

Daniel In The Lions' Den

What happened next?

Trace the broken lines to complete the pictures. Then color the pictures.

Do not be afraid.

When should we pray?

Draw lines to match the phrases with the pictures.

When we work

When we play

When we eat

When we go to bed

Jonah And The Great Fish

Color the picture of Jonah and the fish.

PARENTS discipline because of Love.

Color the pictures of children doing things for which they should be disciplined.

Trace the lines to complete the sentence and the picture. Then color the picture.

Jesus is God.

Cut out baby Jesus and paste Him in the manger.
Cut out the lamb and paste it lying nearby.

Lesson 21 cutouts

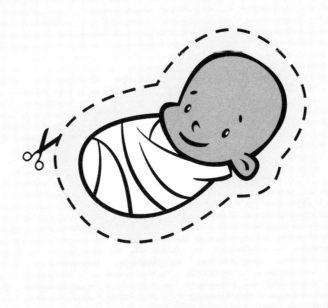

Lesson Twenty-Two
The Shepherds And The Wise Men

Help your teacher read the story by saying the word represented by each picture.

 angel   Mary   Joseph   Bethlehem

baby   donkey   manger   shepherds

An came to . The said, "You will have a . Call Him Jesus." rode on a to . The Jesus was born in . The  Jesus was put in a .

An came to the . The said, "The Jesus is born in and is in a ."

The went to . They saw and . They also saw the baby Jesus in the .

59

Love means giving.

In the blank space, draw a picture of something you can do to show your parents that you love them. Then color the pictures.

Jesus Grows Up

How do we grow?

Cut out the pictures and paste them in the correct box.

I grow taller.

I grow wiser.

I love God.

I love others.

Going To Church

Help the child avoid the obstacles and get to church.

Lesson 23 Cutouts

Jesus Chooses His Helpers

Draw some fish in the fishing net and color them.

What is God's plan for these people?

_____

_____

_____

_____

Write your name in the blank.

God has a special plan for _____.

Jesus And The Children

Paste the pictures of the children in the hearts around Jesus.

Let the little children come to Me (Mark 10:14).

Circle the pictures that describe you.

I am a

I am   4   5   6.

I like to

I like to eat

My name is

_____

All my days are written in Your book (Psalm 139:16).

Lesson 25 cutouts

Zacchaeus And Nicodemus

Jesus saw Zacchaeus in the sycamore tree. Find Zacchaeus and circle him.
Also, find and circle a ship, a tent, and a sword. Then color the tree.

Nicodemus came to Jesus at night. Draw a moon and stars and color them yellow.
Color the sky black. Then color the rest of the picture.

Jesus Heals The Sick

Match the pictures of the people Jesus healed with the pictures of what they were like after Jesus healed them.

Help Bartimaeus find his way to Jesus so he can be healed.

Lesson Twenty-Eight
The Good Shepherd

Connect the dots.

Draw the staff in the shepherd's hand.

Trace the broken lines.

Draw two coins in the innkeeper's hand.

Things Used In Jesus' Time

Write the correct number in each blank.

There are _____ oil lamps.

There are _____ olives.

There are _____wells.

There are _____water jars.

Lesson Twenty-Nine
The House On The Rock

Use these words to finish the sentences.

rock	sand	Jesus

This house was on the _____.

This house was on the _____.

The rock is like _____.

My Life–House

Cut out and paste in pictures that match each part of the house.

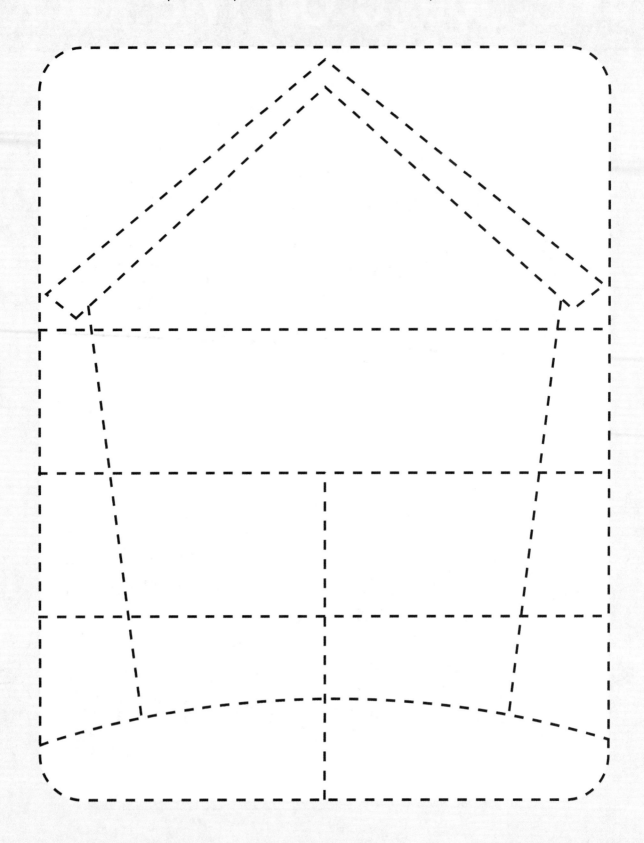

Lesson Thirty
Jesus Dies On The Cross

Jesus died for our sins.

Trace the broken lines to complete the cross on which Jesus died.

King of the Jews

Color the names **red**. Color the numbers **blue**.

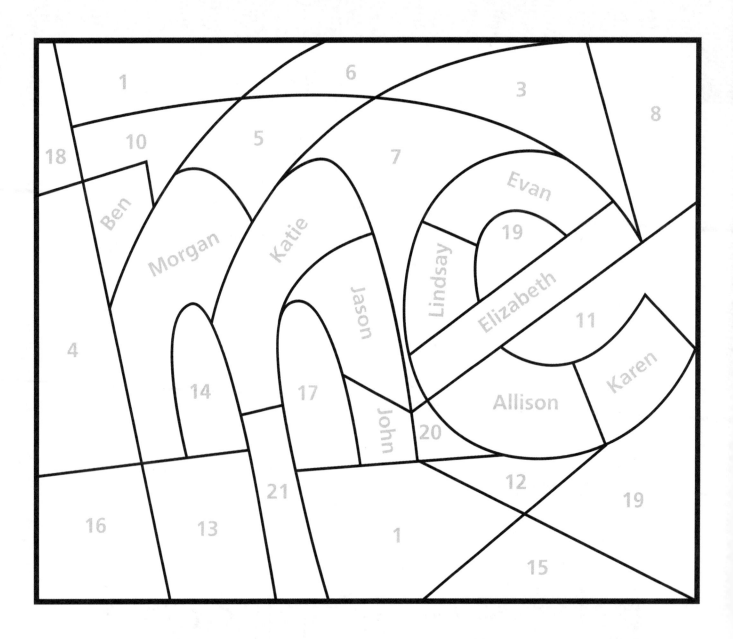

The secret word is _____. Jesus died for _____.

Lesson Thirty-One
Jesus Lives Again!

Follow the dots to see whom the women found at the tomb on Sunday morning instead of Jesus.

Color the picture that shows how most trees look at Easter.

Jesus Begins His Church

Write the correct number in each box to show the order
in which these things happened.

God wants Mike to tell his dad the truth about the window he broke.
Help him find his dad.

Complete the biblical truth in Ephesians 4:25a with these words.

lying   **truth**

Stop_____, and speak _____ to everyone.

Paul—The First Missionary

Add flames and smoke to the jailer's torch. Then color the rest of the picture.

Beginning with the letter "P" in the first note, fill in the blanks with every other letter.

Sing ____ ____ ____ ____ ____ ____ to God (Psalm 47:6a).

Paul Spreads The Gospel

How did God use Paul?

Use these words to complete the statements.

| missionary | churches | letters | gospel |

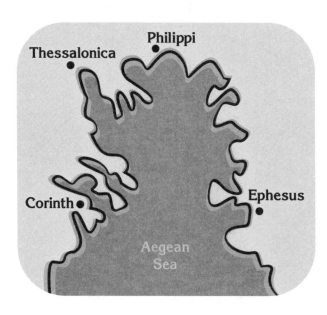

Paul preached the g_____.

Paul started many c_____.

Paul was the first m_____.

Paul wrote l_____ to new Christians.

Paul's Letters became Part of our Bibles.

Match each sentence with the correct picture.

Paul wrote letters.

Men copied God's Word in books.

Today Bibles are sent around the world.

Learing From God's Word

I can be God's servant by...

In the blank space, draw a picture of another way you can be God's servant.
Then color all the pictures.

Do you remember?

Write the correct name from the list under each picture.

| Noah | Joseph | Moses | Samson | Jesus | Paul |

_____   _____   _____

_____   _____   _____

Learning About God
Scripture Memory

Lesson 1	Genesis 1:1, Genesis 1:31b
Lesson 2	1 Peter 5:7b, Psalm 23:1
Lesson 3	1 John 1:9a
Lesson 4	Ephesians 6:1
Lesson 6	Romans 3:23
Lesson 7	Psalm 127:3a
Lesson 8	Ephesians 4:32
Lesson 10	Psalm 139:17a
Lesson 11	Psalm 139:18a
Lesson 12	Psalm 95:6b
Lesson 13	1 John 2:3
Lesson 15	Philippians 4:13
Lesson 16	Proverbs 16:23b
Lesson 17	Proverbs 20:11
Lesson 18-19	Deuteronomy 31:6
Lesson 21	Luke 2:11
Lesson 22	Luke 2:12
Lesson 24	Psalm 100:1
Lesson 25	Psalm 100:2a
Lesson 26	Psalm 100:3a
Lesson 27	Psalm 100:4b
Lesson 28	Psalm 100:5a
Lesson 30-31	1 Corinthians 15:3b-4
Lesson 32	Ephesians 4:25a
Lesson 33	Acts 16:31b
Lesson 34	Mark 16:15b

Sacred Geometry

perfect proportions for optimum relaxation

by Mike Roy

A grown-up coloring book by Color Serenity™

Sacred Geometry

Copyright © Color Serenity

By: Mike Roy

First Edition, February 2016

ISBN-13: 978-1-944943-00-4
ISBN-10: 1-944943-00-5

Visit our website for free printable coloring pages at:
www.colorserenity.com

Questions? Comments? Please email us at:
info@colorserenity.com

Printed in U.S.A.

What is sacred geometry?

Sacred geometry are the naturally occurring patterns found everywhere we look. These universal designs can be found in the nautilus shell, the structure of atoms, and in the magnetic fields of the planets.

From ancient times, humankind has ascribed a spiritual significance to these forms, believing that God created the universe with an underlying geometric plan. Our ancestors studied their mathematical structure, found them inherently sound, and used them in the construction of buildings and objects. The ancient Greeks, among others, adapted their forms into both art and architecture, creating works that still stand today in both physical presence and influence.

The Golden Mean, also called the Golden Ratio, (1:1.61) is one example of such a form. This ratio (like pi or fibonacci numbers) is a naturally occurring mathematical principle that has practical use as well as beauty, and is widely in use by both artists and engineers alike.

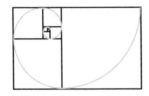

These ratios, forms, and formulas (which can be infinitely complex) don't have to be studied in a scholarly fashion to be appreciated. We can simply sit in peace and gaze at the fractal pattern in a leaf or the radial symmetry of a daisy. When we absorb these forms, much like our skin absorbs vitamins from the energy from our sun, our innermost being resonates and harmonizes with the creation around us.

The book you are holding is a collection of some of the commonly used shapes and patterns associated with sacred geometry. As you direct your hands to apply color to the natural forms in this book, my wish is that you feel that inner peace that comes from being in harmony with the universe that you are an integral part of.

~ Mike Roy

Contents

 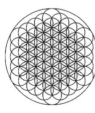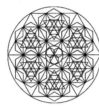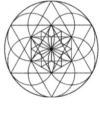

Contents

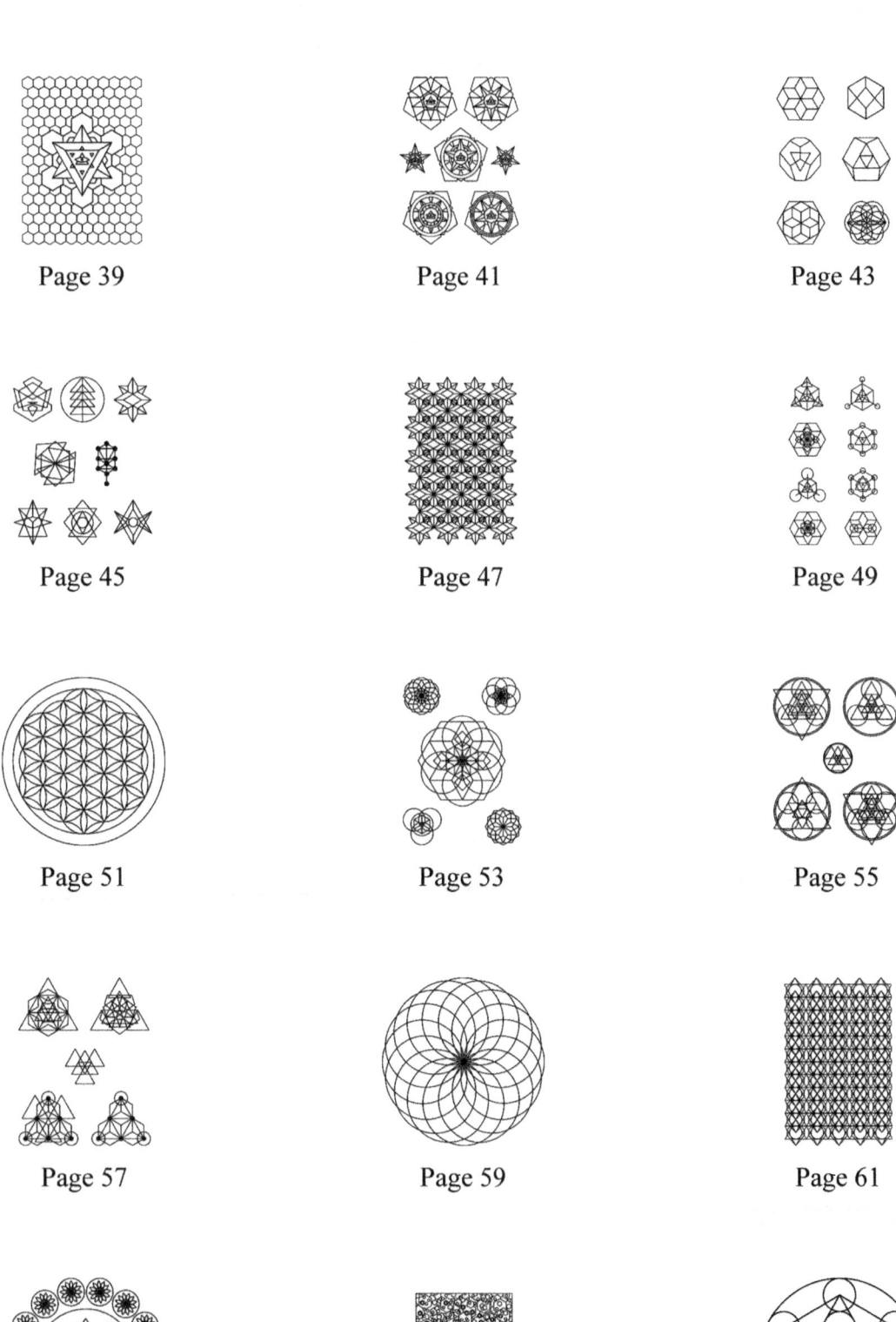

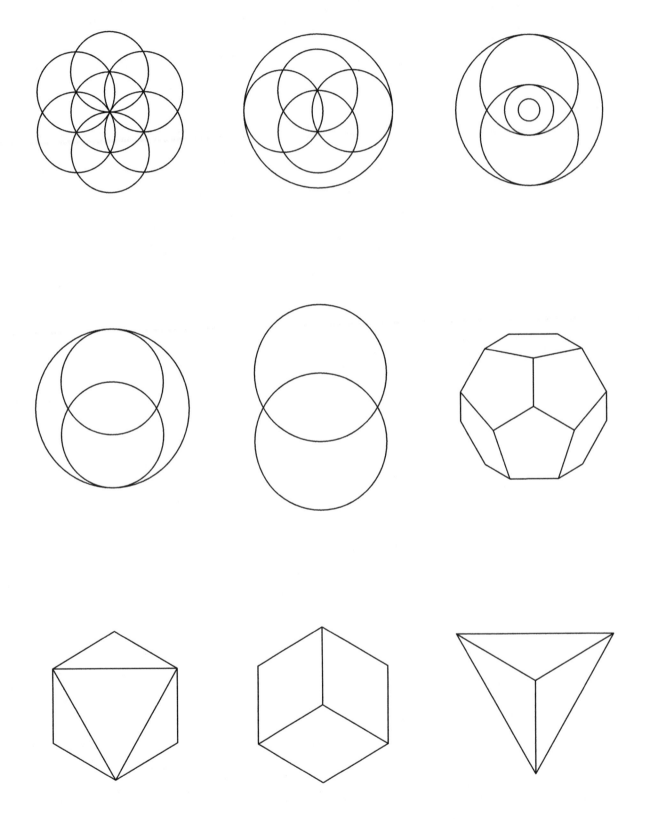

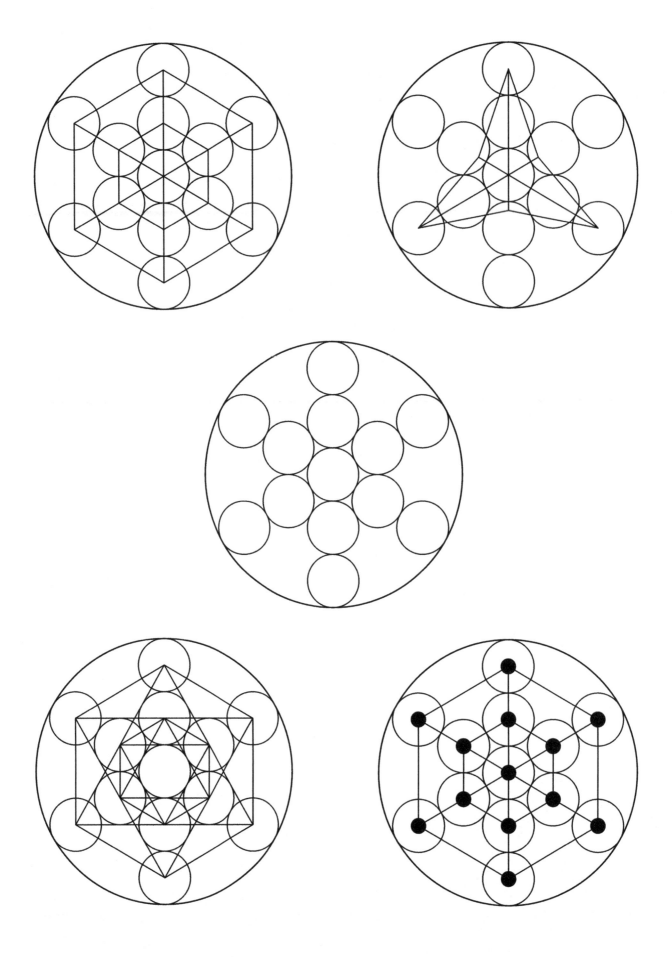

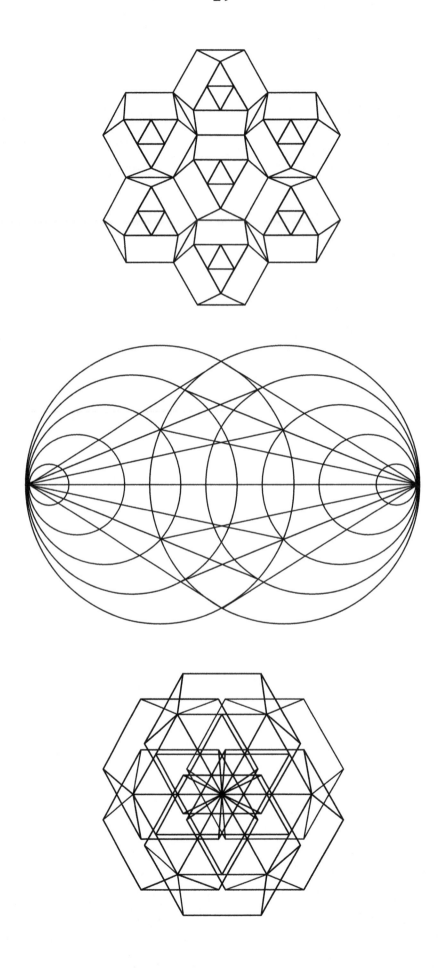

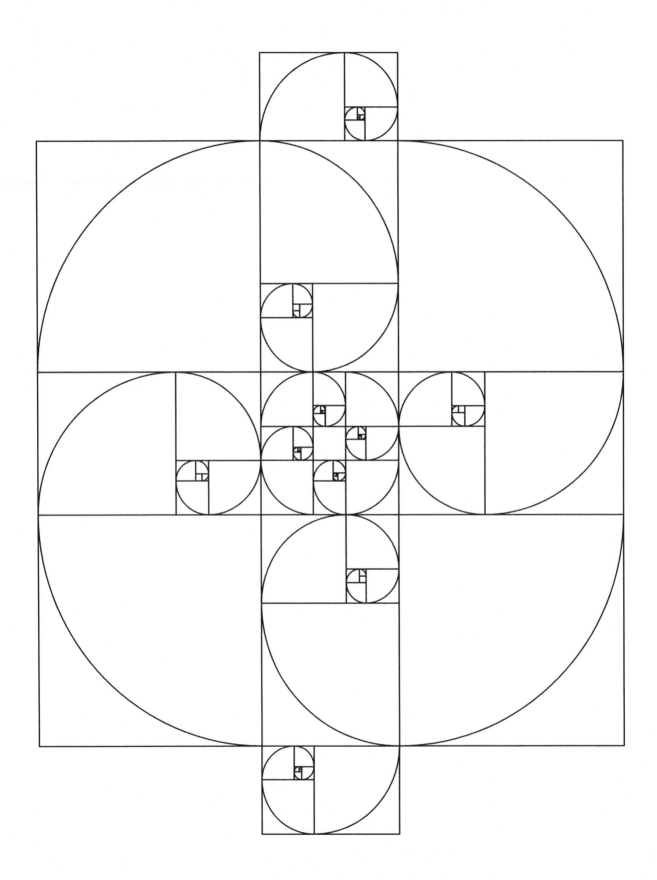

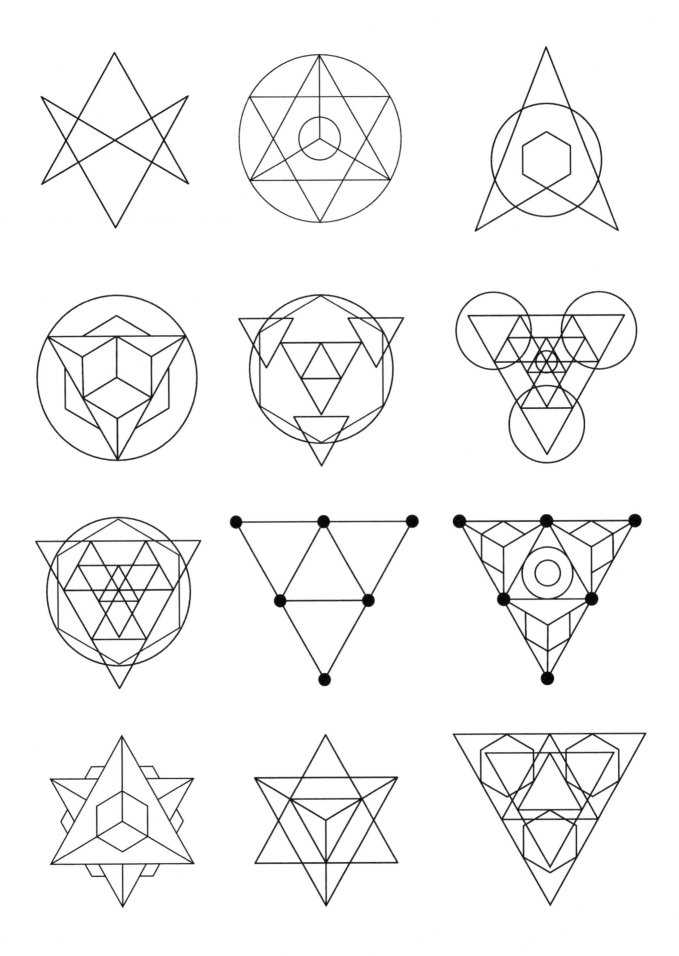

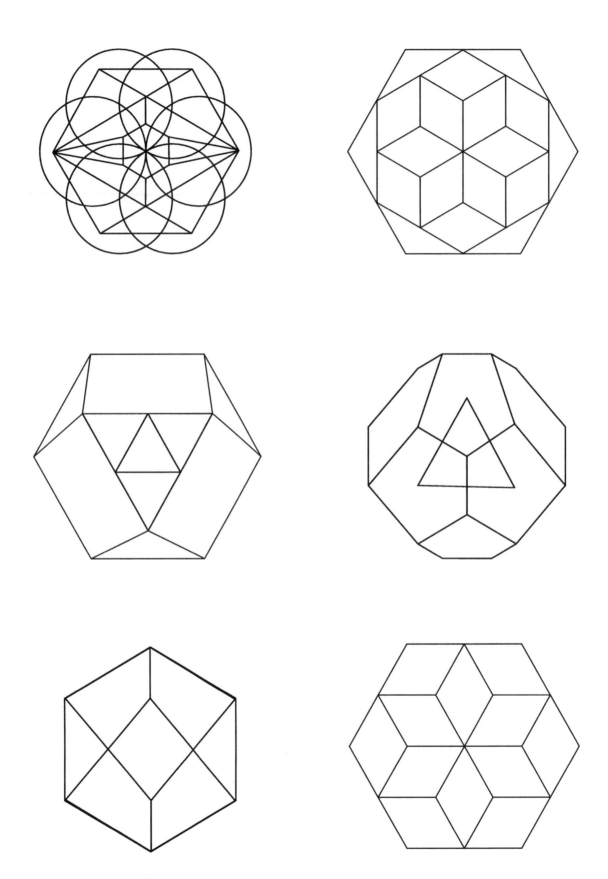

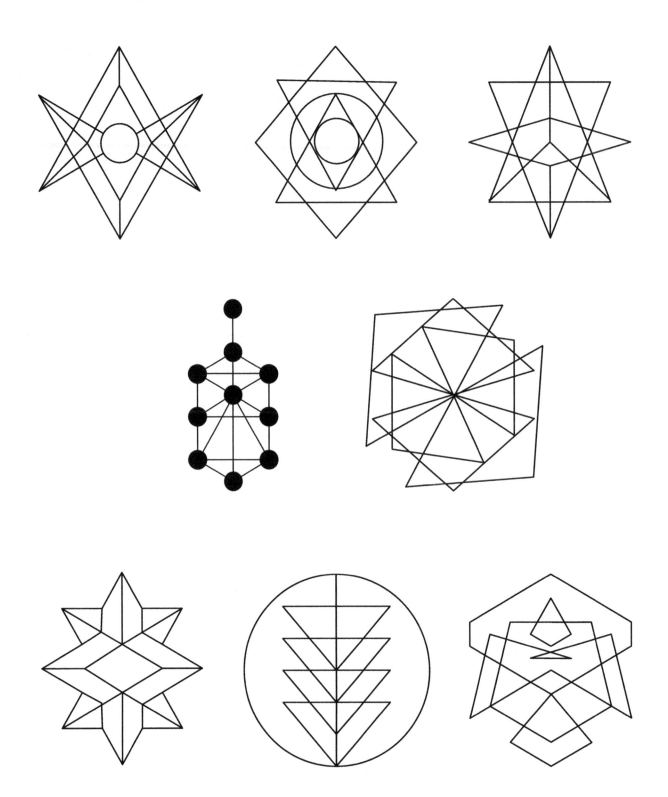

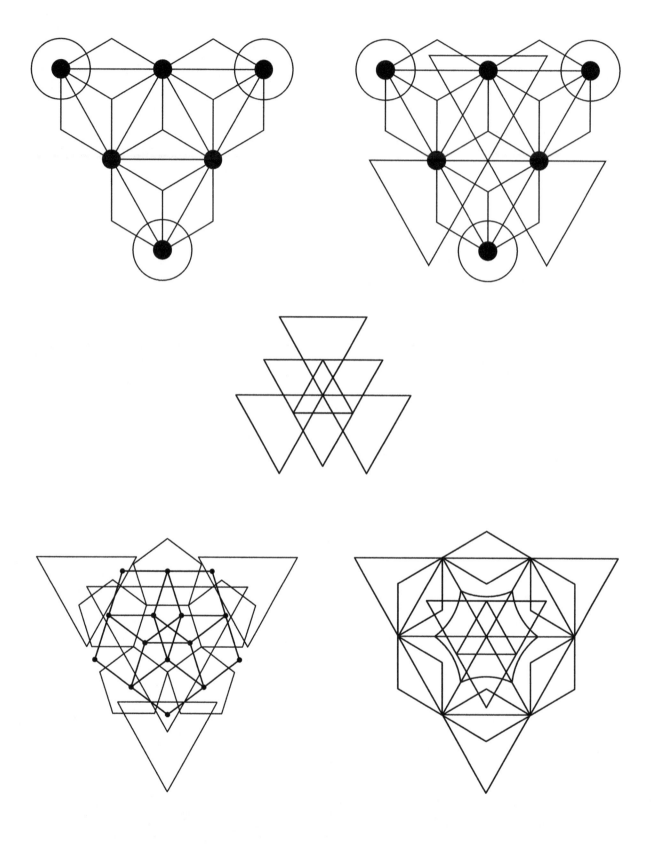

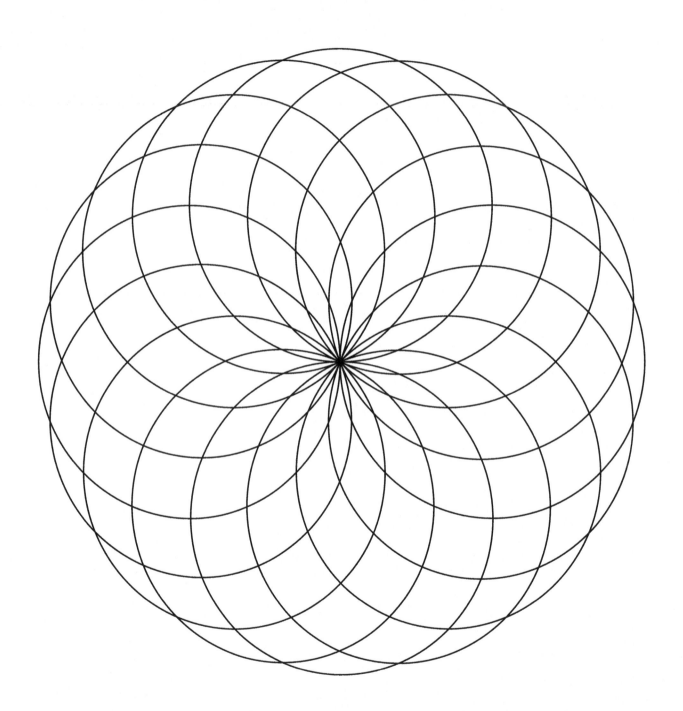

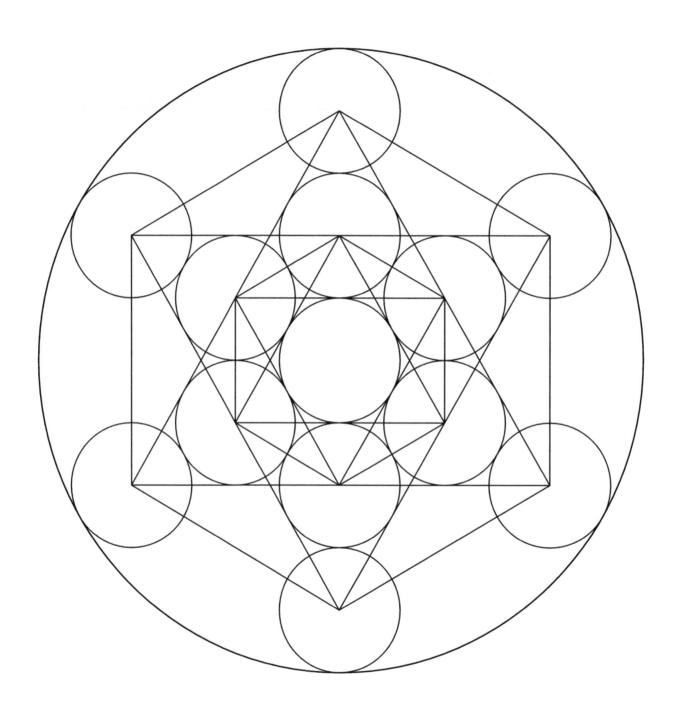

Tips for a Relaxing Coloring Experience

- These pages work with colored pencils, colored markers, and other mediums. Experiment and have fun!

- When using colored pencils, keep the tips sharpened when coloring next to the edges if you want more accuracy.

- Don't press too hard when coloring with pencils… try to build up your color by layers instead.

- For dense, rich color, try laying down colored pencils first and going over that with colored markers.

- Want to add more to the designs? Feel free to grab a black fine-tip pen and add your own doodles in the empty spaces!

- For a visually relaxing color harmony, select neighboring colors on the color wheel for areas that are next to each other in the design. For example, put oranges next to reds and greens next to blues.

- For a more dynamic and energetic composition, select colors opposite each other on the color wheel. For example, purple next to yellow, orange with blue, and green with red. These colors really pop against each other!

- Before you use a color for the first time and are not sure what it will do, try using it on a test piece of paper first.

- Remember, THERE ARE NO RULES… just relax and have fun coloring!

Join the **Serenity Club** today!

Get 30 FREE Coloring Pages *instantly* when you join the **Serenity Club!**
You'll also get some other great benefits when you join:

- Advance notice of future Color Serenity coloring books before they come out
- An "inner circle" of fellow colorists just like you who love to relax through coloring
- Access to Color Serenity specials, coupons, promotions, and giveaways
- The ability to influence the content of future coloring books... your feedback is very important to me!

Don't wait! Join us now at:

www.colorserenity.com/join

Made in the USA
Las Vegas, NV
27 December 2020